Audition Songs for Male Singers
Frank Sinatra

Ten great songs ideal for auditions

Wise Publications
part of The Music Sales Group
London/New York/Paris/Sydney/Copenhagen/Berlin/Madrid/Tokyo

Published by
Wise Publications
8/9 Frith Street,
London W1D 3JB, UK.

Exclusive Distributors:
Music Sales Limited
Distribution Centre, Newmarket Road,
Bury St Edmunds, Suffolk IP33 3YB, UK.
Music Sales Pty Limited
120 Rothschild Avenue,
Rosebery, NSW 2018,
Australia.

Order No. AM985226
ISBN 1-84609-483-6
This book © Copyright 2006 Wise Publications,
a division of Music Sales Limited.

Arranging and Engraving supplied by Camden Music.
Cover photograph courtesy Santi Visalli Inc./Contributor/Getty Images.
Printed in the United Kingdom by
Caligraving Limited, Thetford, Norfolk.

CD recording engineered by Jonas Persson.
Band Arrangements by Christopher Hussey and Jeremy Birchall.
Flute/Alto Saxophone: John Whelan.
Clarinet/Tenor Saxophone: Jamie Talbot.
Horn: Rebecca Taylor.
Trumpets: Tony Fisher & Mike Lovatt.
Trombone: Andy Wood.
Violins: Simon Baggs, Christian Halstead, Anya Birchall, Jeremy Birchall.
Viola: Katherine Shave.
Cello: Louise Dixon, Victoria Walker.
Piano: Gareth Williams.
Keyboards: Christopher Hussey, Ann Farmer & Jonas Persson.
Guitars/Mandolin: Arthur Dick.
Bass: Paul Morgan.
Drums: Ian Thomas & Ralph Salmins.

CD Tracks:

The Best Of Everything
(Kande/Ebb) Carlin Music Corporation.

Come Fly With Me
(Cahn/Van Heusen) The International Music Network Limited/Cherry Lane Music Limited.

Love And Marriage
(Cahn/Van Heusen) The International Music Network Limited/Warner/Chappell Music Limited.

The Girl From Ipanema (Garota De Ipanema)
(Moraes/Jobim) Universal/MCA Music Limited/Windswept Music (London) Limited.

My Way
(Francois/Revaux/Thibaut) Sony/ATV Music Publishing (UK) Limited/Warner/Chappell Music Limited.

New York, New York
(Ebb/Kander) Warner Bros. Publications Incorporated/IMP Limited.

Strangers In The Night
(Singleton/Snyder/Kaempfert) Universal/MCA Music Limited.

That's Life
(Kay/Kelly) Universal Music Publishing Limited.

The Way You Look Tonight
(Fields/Kern) Warner/Chappell Music Limited/Universal Music Publishing Limited.

Somethin' Stupid
(Parks) Montclare Music Company Limited.

The Best Of Everything

Words & Music by John Kander & Fred Ebb

Come Fly With Me

Words by Sammy Cahn
Music by James Van Heusen

1. Come fly with me,___ let's fly,___ let's fly___ a - way!___
(2.) fly with me,___ let's float___ down to___ Pe - ru!___
(3° Instrumental)

If you can use___ some ex -
In Lla - ma Land,___ there's a

an - gels cheer 'cause___ we're to - geth - er. Wea - ther - wise,___ it's such___

___ a love - ly day!_____ Just

say the words,_ and we'll beat the birds___ down to Ac - a - pul - co

Bay. It's per - fect for___ a fly - ing ho - ney - moon,___

13

Love And Marriage

Words by Sammy Cahn
Music by James Van Heusen

1. Love and mar - riage, love and mar - riage, they go to - geth - er like a
2. Love and mar - riage, love and mar - riage, it's an in - sti - tute you
3. Love and mar - riage, love and mar - riage, they go to - geth - er like a

To Coda ⊕

horse and car - riage.
can't dis - pa - rage.
horse and car - riage.

This I'll tell you, broth - er: you
Ask the lo - cal gen - try, and
Dad was told by Moth - er "You

1.
can't have one with-out the oth - er.

2.
- ment - 'ry.

they will say it's e - le -

Try, try, try to se - pa - rate them; it's an____ il -

16

The Girl From Ipanema
(Garota De Ipanema)

Words by Vinicius De Moraes
Music by Antonio Carlos Jobim

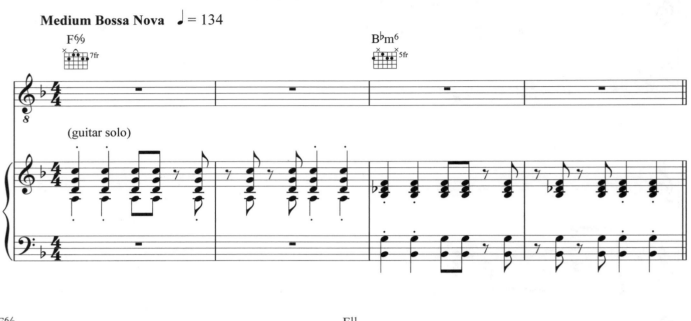

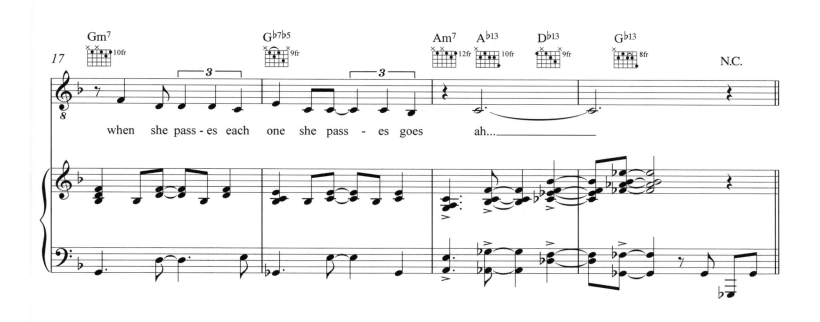

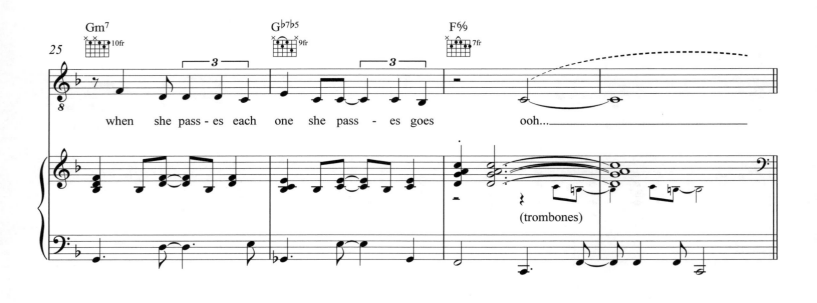

when she pass-es each one she pass-es goes ooh...

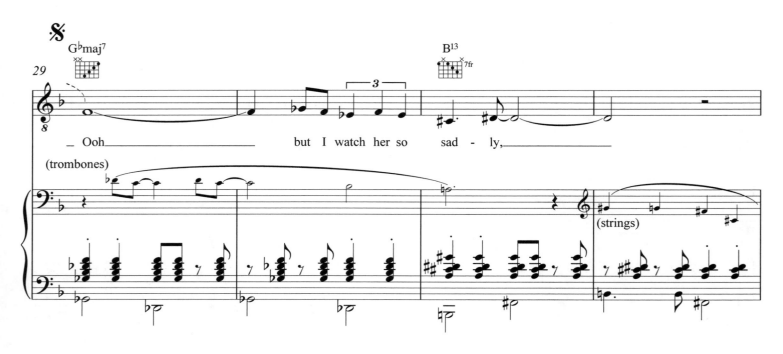

_ Ooh_____ but I watch her so sad-ly,_____

(trombones)

(strings)

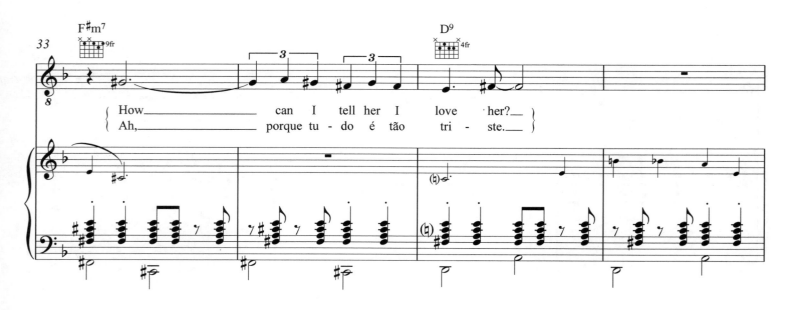

{ How_____ can I tell her I love her?_ }
{ Ah,_____ porque tu-do é tão tri-ste._ }

Yes,_____ I would give my heart glad - ly,____

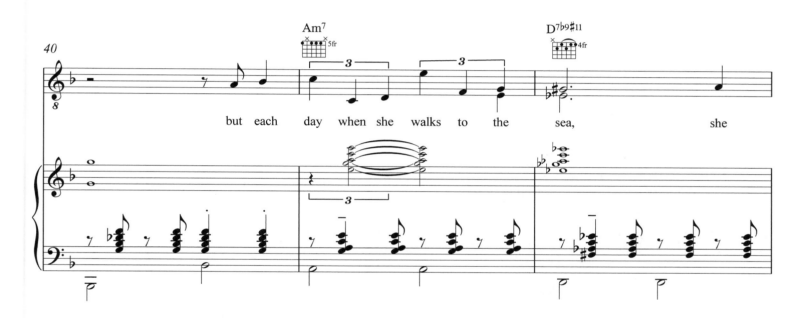

but each day when she walks to the sea, she

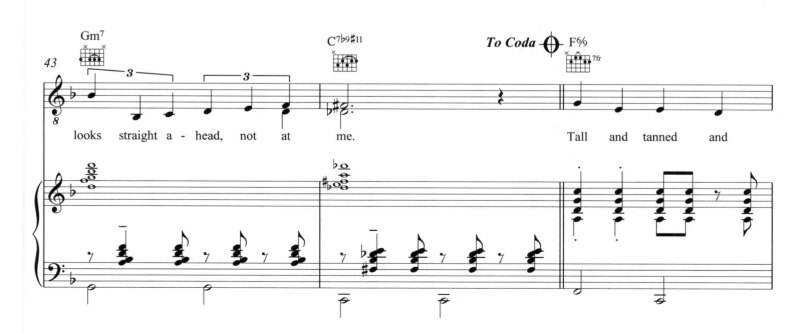

looks straight a - head, not at me. Tall and tanned and

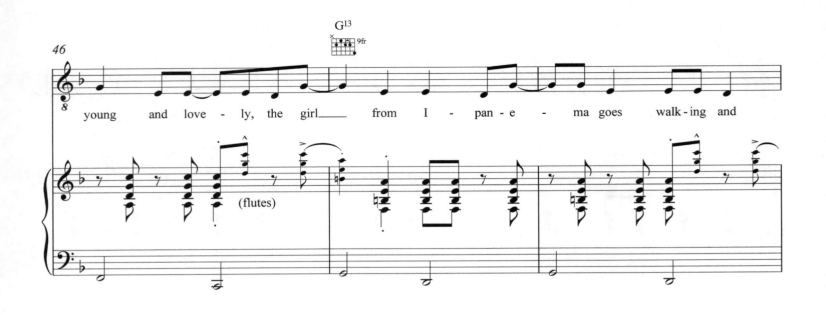

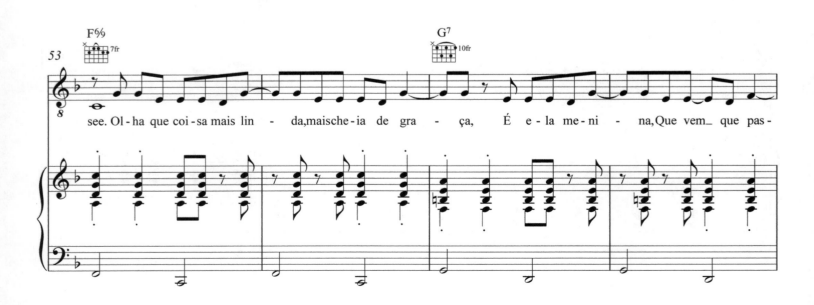

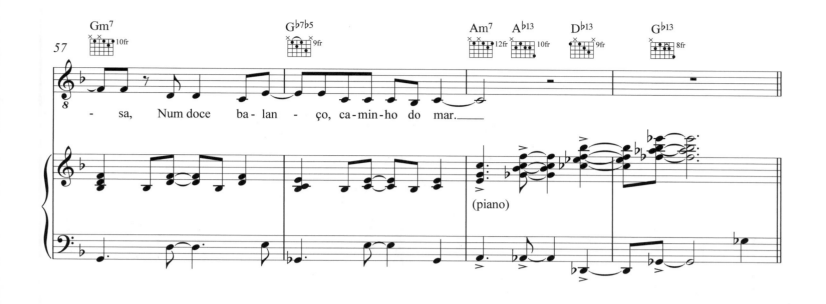

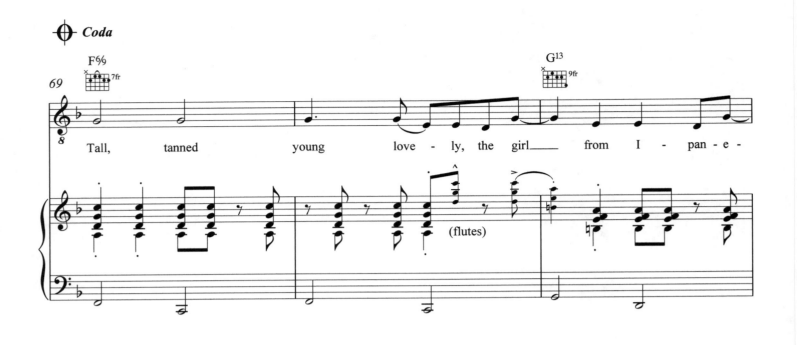

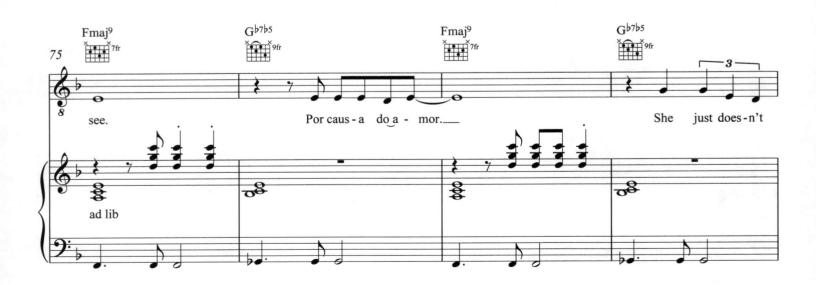

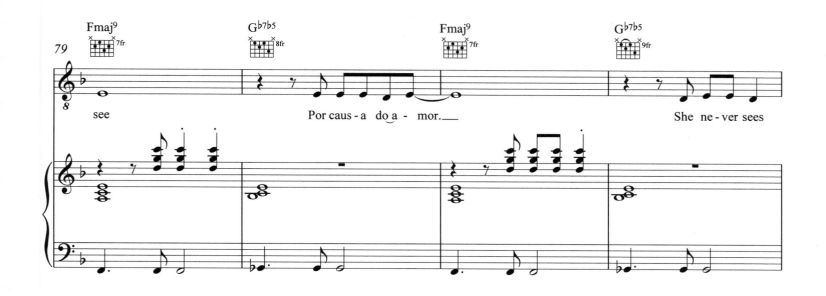

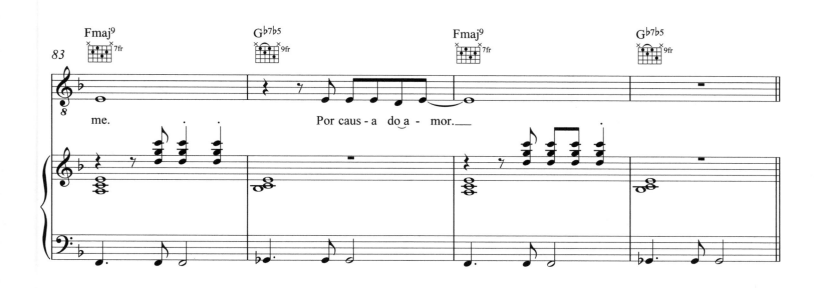

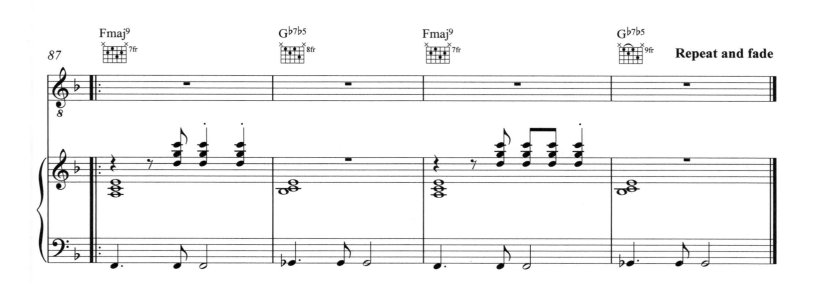

My Way

Words & Music by Claude Francois, Jacques Revaux & Gilles Thibaut

New York, New York

Words by Fred Ebb
Music by John Kander

New York,__ New York!__

I want to wake up__ in a ci-ty that nev-er sleeps,__

and find I'm A num-ber one,__

top of the list, king of the hill, A num-ber one.

These lit-tle town blues

are melt-ing a way. I'm gon-na make a brand

new start of it in old New York.

34

Strangers In The Night

Words by Charles Singleton & Eddie Snyder
Music by Bert Kaempfert

Stran-gers in the night _____ ex-chang-ing glan - ces,

wond-'ring in the night _____ what were the chan - ces we'd be shar-ing love _____

That's Life

Words & Music by Dean Kay & Gordon Kelly

The Way You Look Tonight

Words by Dorothy Fields
Music by Jerome Kern

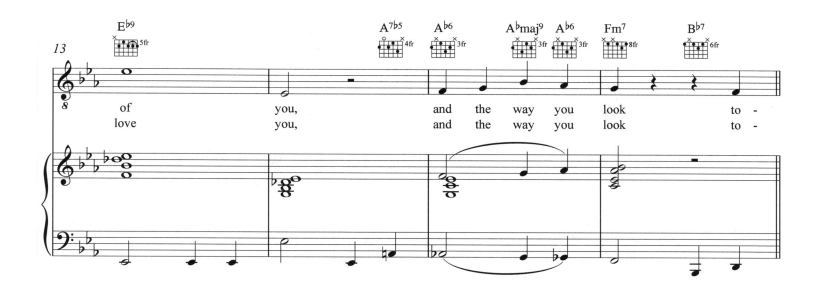

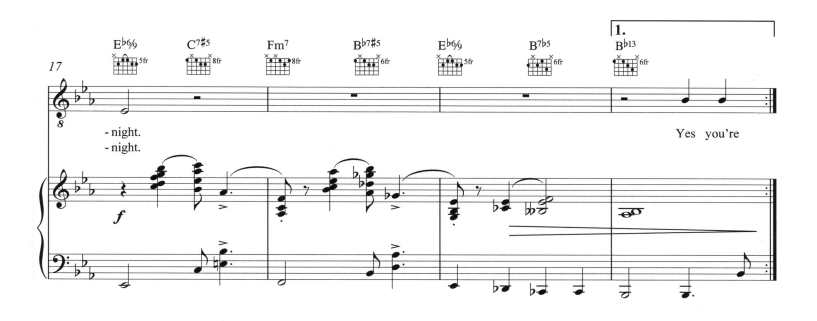

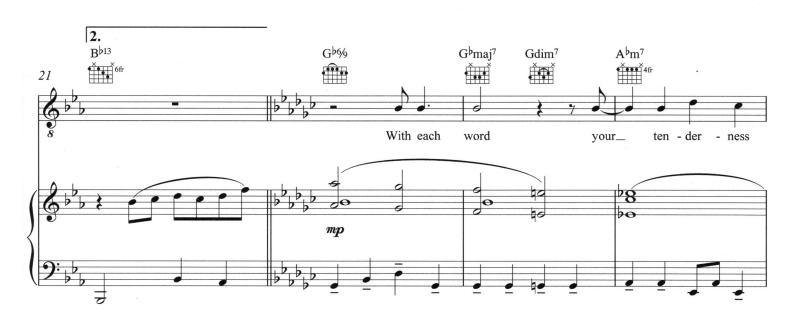

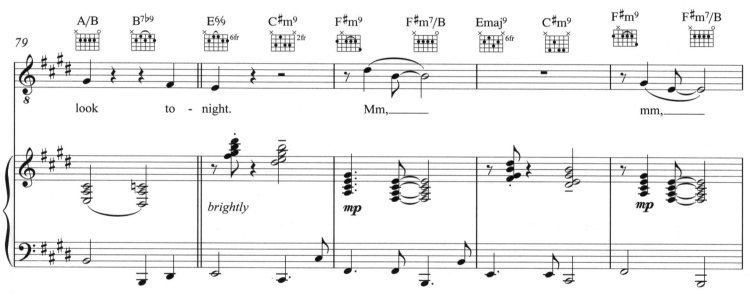

rall. to end

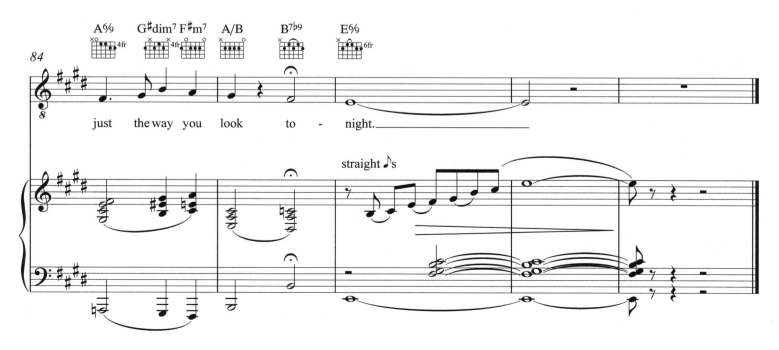

Somethin' Stupid

Words & Music by C. Carson Parks

know I stand in line un - til you think you have the time to spend an

ev-'ning with me,___ and if we go some place to dance I

know that there's a chance you won't be leav-ing with me.___

Then af-ter-wards we drop in-to a qui-et lit-tle place and have a

drink or two,___ and then I go and spoil it all__ by

123456789